Contents

Seek and Find

Can you find these objects in your book?

page 5

page 19

page 21

page 23

page 9

page 27

Solving Hidden Pictures puzzles develops figure-ground perception and improves the ability to establish object constancy and size relationships. Educators have shown that working on these puzzles can enhance a child's attention to detail, reinforce good work habits, increase word knowledge, and aid in developing self-confidence.

comb

crayon

caterpillar

cucumber

car

cup

carrot

crown

candle

cap

Illustrated by Valeri Gorbachev

Try to write some of your favorite words that begin with C on the lines below.

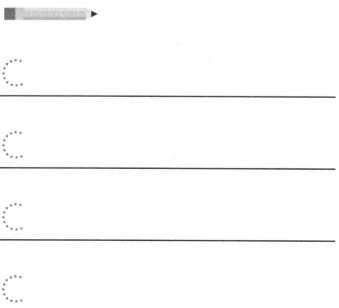

C _____

C _____

C _____

C _____

Can you find the 10 objects hidden in the picture that begin with the letter c? Cool! Answers on page 30

3

These 8 funny things are happening in the scene. Can you find them all?

Answers on page 30

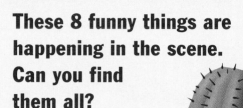

Imagine and Draw

What is the silliest thing you might find riding on a horse? Draw a picture of it here.

CRAYON

Illustrated by Nathan Y. Jarvis

Carlos and Maria are teaching their dog, Barney, to play catch.

Can you find these hidden objects on the next page?

Answers on page 30

mouse

spoon

slice of pizza

slice of bread

pickle

broom

key

pan

Illustrated by Larry DiFiori

Can you guess the answer to each riddle? Use the Hidden Pictures® words if you need help.

When a door cannot be opened,

You unlock it using me.

I live in a pocket or a purse.

I am a shiny _____.

I am a tiny animal,

Hiding in a hole or house.

You know me by my squeaky sound.

That's right. I am a _____.

If your floor is getting dusty,

Use me to sweep the room.

My bristles can be made of straw.

I am a wooden _____.

Use me to make a sandwich

Or a piece of toast instead.

I might be white or wheat or rye.

I am a _____.

Can you find the Hidden Pictures below? When you finish, you can color in the

rest of the scene. || CRAYON || Answers on page 30   Illustrated by R. Michael Palan

Color in a heart in this box each time you find a heart in the picture. ▌▌ CRAYON ▌▌

1 2 3 4 5

6 7 8 9 10

Use your crayons to decorate this valentine.
▌▌ CRAYON ▌▌

TO_____

FROM_____

At the clock shop, Mr. Harris fixes all kinds of clocks and watches.

Can you find 8 Hidden Pictures® on the next page? Answers on page 31

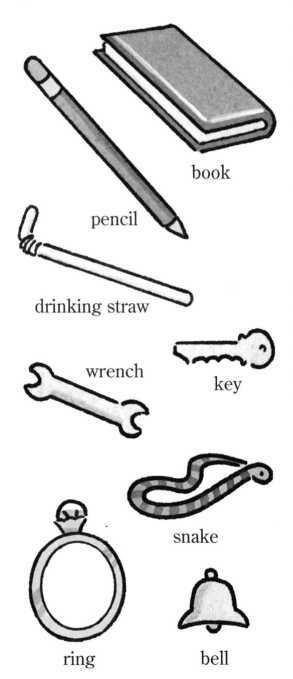

book

pencil

drinking straw

wrench

key

snake

ring

bell

Connect the dots from Ⓐ to Ⓩ. When you finish, you will see an interesting kind of clock. ◼▬▬►

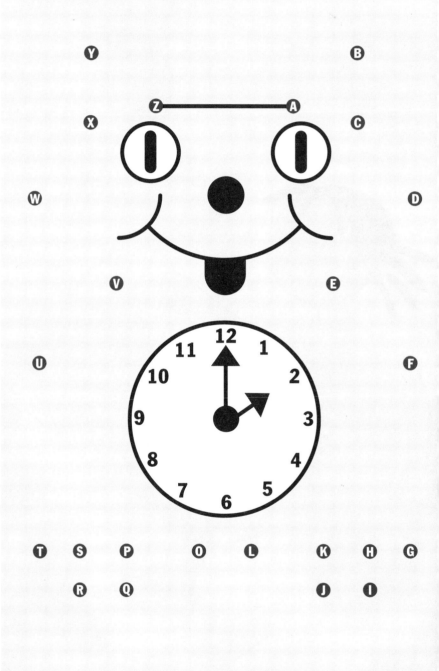

The Anderson family is having their annual yard sale.
Do you see anything you might like to buy?

Can you find these Hidden Pictures® on the next page? Answers on page 31

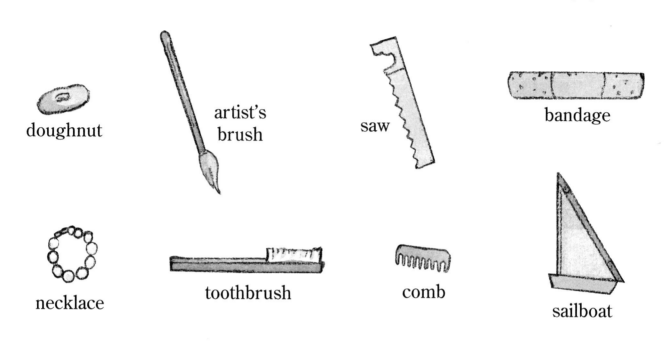

doughnut

artist's brush

saw

bandage

necklace

toothbrush

comb

sailboat

Illustrated by Philomena O'Neill

Scavenger Hunt Here are some more things to find:

A butterfly

Three toy animals

Two pairs of eyeglasses

A baseball

A tennis racket

Three teacups

An empty fishbowl

Eight red flowers

Can you find the Hidden Pictures below? When you finish, you can color in the

Anthony and his mom have bought a lot of his favorite foods at the store.

Can you find these items in the picture on the next page? Be sure to find the right number of each.

Answers on page 31

1 milk carton

2 cereal boxes

3 juice boxes

4 cans of soup

5 apples

6 oranges

Illustrated by Monica Wellington

Color in each shape that has a green dot with a green crayon.

| CRAYON |

Color in each shape that has an orange dot with an orange crayon.

| CRAYON |

When you finish, you will see something that you might find at the market.

What good's a thumb? I know. Do you?
It does great things. Here are a few.
It helps you open a book so you can read it
Or peel a banana so you can eat it.

You need a thumb if it's your wish
To hold a rod and catch a fish,
Pick up a pencil and start to scribble,
Or lift a fork and start to nibble,

Grab a baseball and give it a toss,
Or clean your teeth with a piece of floss.
To make a braid or comb your hair,
You need a thumb—that's why it's there.

All these uses and many more—
I've learned because my thumb is sore.
So if sometime your thumb hurts, too,
Take my advice, here's what to do:

Ask Mom to help you with your sweater
And with your buttons—you'll have to let her.
If you should sneeze and say *aah-choo,*
Let Daddy blow your nose for you.

Use both your hands to hold your cup
Till you can give the old "thumbs-up."
And in that special way you'll say,
"Hooray, my thumb is A-OK!"

After you finish the poem, see if you can find these 8 Hidden Pictures in the scene.

Answers on page 32

A Hidden Pictures® Poem by Patricia Millman

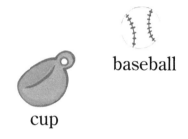

baseball

cup

pencil

fork

banana

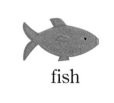

book

fish

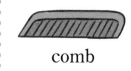

comb

Illustrated by Barbara Lipp

cupcake

boot

lollipop

apple

mitten

key

Each object is hidden two times—once in each scene. We found and circled the mittens. Can you find the others? Answers on page 32

flag

horseshoe

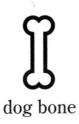
dog bone

pickle

shoe

pear

Can you find the Hidden Pictures below? When you finish, you can color in the

rest of the scene. || CRAYON || Answers on page 32

Illustrated by Timothy Davis

Leo the artist has taken his paints to the park.
He is drawing a picture of what he sees there.

Can you find these shapes in the picture on the next page? Answers on page 32

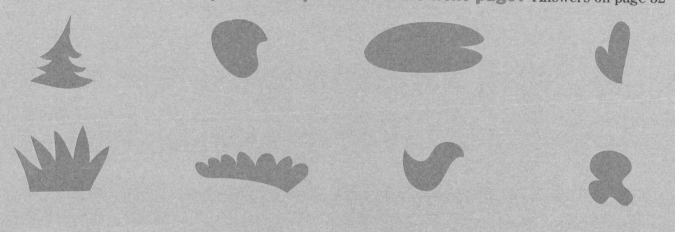

What do you see when you go to the park?

Draw a picture of it here.

CRAYON

Be sure to write your name on your drawing when you are finished.

Hidden Pictures®

The juggler tosses 4 balls in the air and never drops a single one!

There are 12 objects hidden in this picture. How many can you find?

Answers on page 32

cup

banana

ladder

moon

boot

candy

fork

heart

horseshoe

crown

mouse

arrow

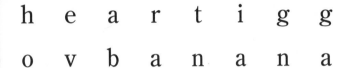

The names of the 12 objects
are hidden below. Some are across.
Others are up and down.
Find and circle each word.

h	e	a	r	t	i	g	g
o	v	b	a	n	a	n	a
r	c	a	n	d	y	z	r
s	l	a	d	d	e	r	r
e	j	i	v	z	i	z	o
s	c	b	o	o	t	i	w
h	u	z	z	i	g	q	m
o	p	f	o	r	k	q	o
e	m	o	u	s	e	i	o
z	i	q	c	r	o	w	n

Answers

Cover

Hidden Pictures® ABC pages 2–3

Silly Cowboys page 5

Smart Dog pages 6–7

When a door cannot be opened,
You unlock it using me.
I live in a pocket or a purse.
I am a shiny **key**.

I am a tiny animal,
Hiding in a hole or house.
You know me by my squeaky sound.
That's right. I am a **mouse**.

If your floor is getting dusty,
Use me to sweep the room.
My bristles can be made of straw.
I am a wooden **broom**.

Use me to make a sandwich
Or a piece of toast instead.
I might be white or wheat or rye.
I am a **slice of bread**.

Roller Coaster pages 8–9

Heart Search page 11

Clock Shop pages 12–13

It's a cat!

Yard Sale pages 14–15

Building pages 16–17

Scavenger Hunt

A butterfly
Look in the tree.

Three toy animals
Two are in a box. One is on the table.

Two pairs of eyeglasses
The boy is wearing a pair. One pair is on the table.

A baseball
Look in the wagon.

A tennis racket
The boy is holding it.

Three teacups
Two are next to a box of books. One is near the teapot.

An empty fishbowl
It is on the table.

Eight red flowers
Look under the window.

Food Find pages 18–19

It's a pineapple!

Answers

What Good's a Thumb? page 21

Double Hidden Pictures® pages 22–23

In the Ocean pages 24–25

Find the Shapes page 27

Hidden Pictures Hidden Words pages 28–29